This book belongs to ...

....

Up You Go and Other Stories

How this collection works

This Read with Biff, Chip and Kipper collection is the first in the series at Level 1. It is divided into two distinct halves.

The first half focuses on phonics-based reading practice, with two phonic activity books: *Kipper's Alphabet I Spy* and *Chip's Letter Sounds*. The second half contains four stories that use everyday language. These stories help to broaden your child's wider reading experience. There are fun activities to enjoy throughout the book.

How to use this book

Find a time to read with your child when they are not too tired and are happy to concentrate for about ten minutes. Reading at this stage should be a shared and enjoyable experience. It is best to choose just one of the activity books or one of the stories using everyday language for each session.

There are tips for reading together for each part of the book. The phonics tips are on pages 6 and 28. They show you how to introduce your child to the phonics activities. Tips to tell you how you can best approach reading the stories with a wider vocabulary are given on pages 50 and 72.

Enjoy sharing the stories!

The **Helping Your Child to Read** handbook contains a wealth of practical information, tips and activities.

OXFORD

UNIVERSITY PRESS

Great Clarendon Street, Oxford, OX2 6DP,
United Kingdom

Oxford University Press is a department of the University of Oxford.
It furthers the University's objective of excellence in research, scholarship,
and education by publishing worldwide. Oxford is a registered trade mark of
Oxford University Press in the UK and in certain other countries

ISBN: 978-0-19-279363-8

5 7 9 10 8 6

Typeset in Edbaskerville

Paper used in the production of this book is a natural, recyclable product made
from wood grown in sustainable forests. The manufacturing process conforms
to the environmental regulations of the country of origin.

Acknowledgements;
Series Editors: Kate Ruttle, Annemarie Young

READ WITH
Biff,
Chip &
Kipper

Up You Go
and Other Stories

OXFORD
UNIVERSITY PRESS

Tips for Reading *Kipper's Alphabet I Spy*

Children learn best when they are having fun.

- Tell your child they are going to help Kipper play 'I spy'.

- For each left hand page, introduce the alphabet letter by saying the sound clearly, e.g. for 'b' say *buh* not *bee*. You can listen to the letter sounds on www.oxfordowl.co.uk.

- Ask your child to trace the letter while repeating the letter sound.

- Then ask them to 'spy' objects on the opposite page starting with the letter.

- Ask them to say what the objects are, and repeat the word slowly, emphasising the sound of the initial letter.

- Give lots of praise as your child plays the game with you.

- Do the animal tracks puzzle on every page and the maze on page 26.

Have fun!

Match the animal tracks on each left hand page to one of the creatures on the right hand page.

This book introduces the letters and sounds of the alphabet:
a b c d e f g h i j k l m n o p q r s t u v w x y z

For more hints and tips on helping your child become a successful and enthusiastic reader look at our website www.oxfordowl.co.uk.

Kipper's Alphabet I Spy

d

I spy with my little eye, something beginning with...

a

b

c

apple, ant, Biff, banana, ball, cat, candle

d e

f

dinosaur, duck, egg, elephant, Floppy, feather

goose, goat, gate, hair, hat, horse, insect

12

j k

l

jelly, jigsaw, Kipper, key, kangaroo, ladybird, lion

14

moon, monkey, milk, nose, nail, net

16

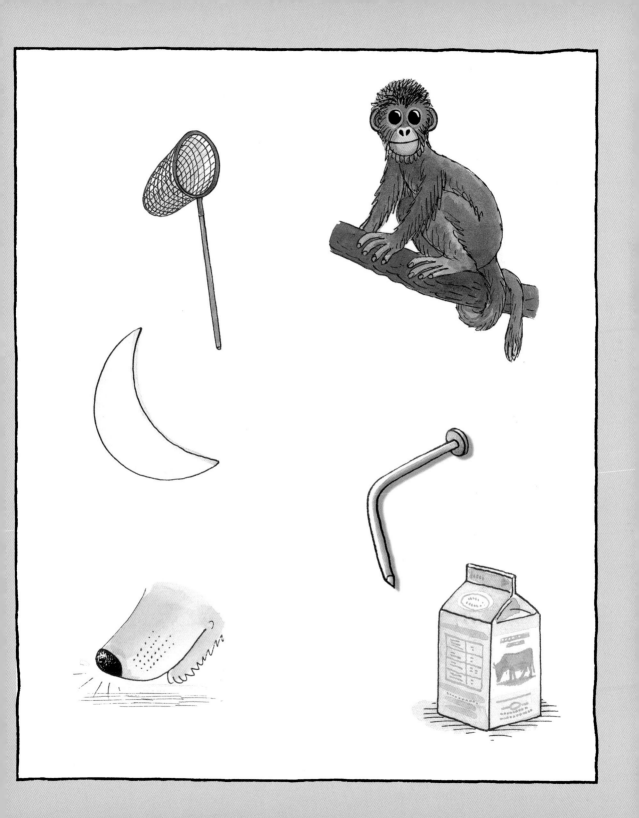

orange, octopus, pear, penguin, purple, queen, quilt

red, rabbit, rainbow, sandwich, sun, tiger, teddy, t-shirt

20

umbrella, under, volcano, violin, watermelon, watch

22

fox, box, yellow, yo-yo, yawn, zebra, zigzag

A maze

Help Kipper get to Floppy.

Tips for Reading *Chip's Letter Sounds*

Children learn best when they are having fun.

- Tell your child they are going to help Chip play 'I spy'.

- For each left hand page, remind your child of the letters by saying the sounds clearly, e.g. for 'b' say *buh* not *bee*. You can listen to the letter sounds on www.oxfordowl.co.uk.

- Ask them to trace the letters with their fingers while repeating the letter sound.

- Then ask your child to 'spy' things on the opposite page which begin with that letter sound. Look for lots of words!

- From page 10 enough letters have been introduced to make whole words. Read the 'word trail' with your child. Sound out each word then say the word (e.g. *h-o-p*, *hop*).

- Do the odd one out puzzle on each page and the tangled lines activity on page 48.

Have fun!

Find the odd one out on every left hand page.

This book practises these letter sounds:

s a t p i n m d g o c k ck
e u r h b f l ff ss

For more hints and tips on helping your child become a successful and enthusiastic reader look at our website www.oxfordowl.co.uk.

Chip's
Letter Sounds

Trace the letters.
Say the sound.

sun, sea, sand, sandwiches, socks, sandals, spade,
seagulls, sandcastle, straw, sails

Look for ten things in this picture that begin with **s**.

table, teapot, tray, towels, tent, train, tools, tractor, tennis racket/ball, tail

presents, paints, picture, penguins, parrot, panda,
polar bear, pop, pin, parents, pen

Say the sounds and then say the words.

s i t   p a t

ill, ink, insects, apple, ambulance, ant, animals,
bat, fan, hat, man, lamp, pat, rat, cat, fin, pillow

Say the sounds and then say the words.

m a n   p i n   n e t

night, necklace, newspaper, needle, net, moon,
Mum, mug, mice, monster, monkeys

Look for all the things in the picture that begin with **m** and **n**.

Say the sounds and then say the words.

d o g D a d g a p

game, garden, green, girl, grass, goal, goldfish,
Dad, dinosaur, doll, dog, octopus, oranges

c C

k K

e E

Say the sounds and then say the words.

p a n   m o p

e gg   s o ck

cake, cook, caterpillar, competition, cat, car, castle, crown,
cream, crocodile, cup, kangaroo, kitchen, eggs, elephant

43

Say the sounds and then say the words.

h o p   m u g
r u b   r o c k

umbrella, rain, red, rabbit, river, rocks, holiday, head, hat, house,
horse, hop, hair, house, hug, rub, Mum, mug, tree trunk

How many things can you find in the picture that begin with **u**, **r** or **h**? Can you find anything with **u** in the middle of the word?

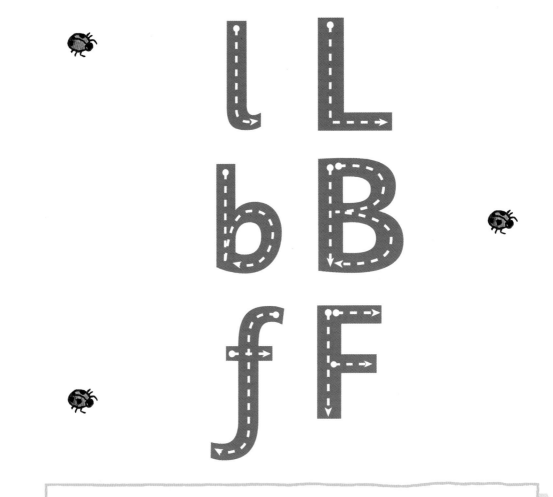

Say the sounds and then say the words.

l e g   b i n
B i ff   m e ss

lady, lolly, leaf, litter, ladybird, flower, bee, butterfly, bench,
bin, biscuit, baby, buggy, balloon, bag, buildings

What things can you find in the picture that begin with **l**, **b** or **f**?

Tangled lines

Follow the lines to find the objects.

Stories for Wider Reading

Tips for Reading *Up You Go* and *I See*

These two stories use simple everyday language. Some of the words used are not decodable, but you can help your child to read them in the context of the story.

- For each story, talk about the title and look through the pictures so that your child can see what each one is about.

- Read the story to your child, placing your finger under each word as you read.

- Read the story again and encourage your child to join in.

- Give lots of praise as your child reads with you.

- Talk about the story and do the fun activity at the end of each story.

Have fun!

After you have read *Up You Go*, find the bee in each picture.

This book includes these useful common words:

go   no   I   Dad   up

50

Up You Go

Up you go, Kipper.

Go!

Up you go, Biff.

Go, go!

Chip, up you go.

Go, go, go!

No, Dad.

No, no, no!

Talk about the story

Who went down the slide first?

What did Dad do to the paddling pool?

Why was Biff laughing at Dad?

Which games do you like to play in the garden?

Spot the difference

Find the five differences in the two pictures of Kipper in the paddling pool.

I See

I see Biff.

I see Chip.

I see Mum and Dad.

We see Kipper.

We see Floppy.

I see Biff and Chip.

I see me!

Biff

 Chip

Mum and Dad

Kipper

Floppy

Biff and Chip

68

Talk about the story

Where was Floppy?

How did Kipper look at Chip?

What was funny about Kipper's glasses?

What do you like to take photos of?

Matching

Help Kipper put the coloured shapes into the right holes.

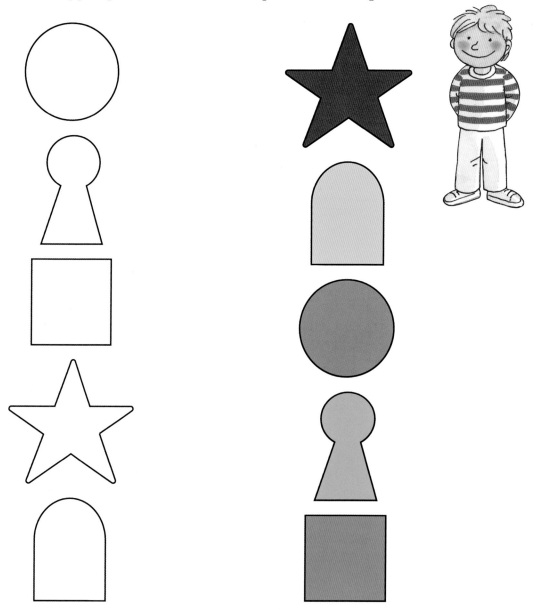

Tips for Reading *Get On* and *Who Can You See?*

These two stories use simple everyday language. Some of the words used are not decodable, but you can help your child to read them in the context of the story.

- For each story, talk about the title and look through the pictures so that your child can see what each one is about.

- Read the story to your child, placing your finger under each word as you read.

- Read the story again and encourage your child to join in.

- Give lots of praise as your child reads with you.

- Talk about the story and do the fun activity at the end of each story.

Children enjoy re-reading stories and this helps to build their confidence.

Have fun!

After you have read *Get On*, find a shell in each picture.

This book includes these useful common words:
get   on   got   and

For more hints and tips on helping your child become a successful and enthusiastic reader look at our website www.oxfordowl.co.uk.

Get On

Written by Roderick Hunt
Illustrated by Alex Brychta

Get on.

Get on, Biff.

Biff got on.

Get on, Chip.

Chip got on.

Get on, Kipper.

Kipper got on.

Oh, no!

Talk about the story

A maze

Help Biff and Chip get to the sea.

Who Can You See?

Written by Roderick Hunt

Illustrated by Alex Brychta

Who can you see?

Biff…

...and Chip.

Mum…

...and Kipper.

Floppy…

...and a spaceman.

No. It is Dad!

Talk about the story

Where was the family?

What shape did Chip make with his hands?

What was Dad wearing?

Which shapes can you make with your shadow?

Match the shadows

Can you match the shadows to the characters?

The UK's best-selling home reading series

Phonics activities and stories help children practise their sounds and letters, as they learn to do in school.

Stories for wider reading have been specially written using everyday language to provide a broader reading experience for your child.

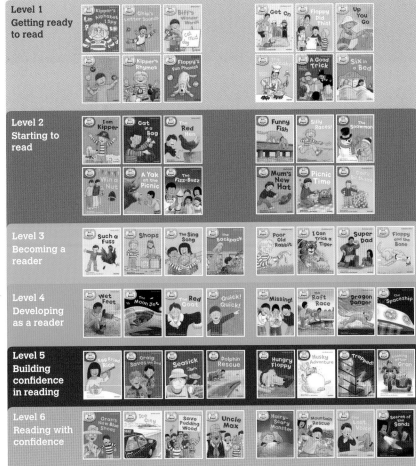

Level 1
Getting ready to read

Kipper's Alphabet I Spy · Chip's Letter Sounds · Biff's Wonder Words · Get On · Floppy Did This! · Up You Go · Kipper's Rhymes · Floppy's Fun Phonics · A Good Trick · Six in a Bed

Level 2
Starting to read

I am Kipper · Cat in a Bag · The Red Hen · Funny Fish · Silly Races! · The Snowman · In a Nut · A Yak at the Picnic · The Fizz-Buzz · Mum's New Hat · Picnic Time · Dad's Plan

Level 3
Becoming a reader

Such a Fuss · Shops · The Sing Song · The Backpack · Poor Old Rabbit · I Can Trick a Tiger · Super Dad · Floppy and the Bone

Level 4
Developing as a reader

Wet Feet · The Moon Jet · The Red Goat · Quick! Quick! · Missing! · The Raft Race · Dragon Danger · The Spaceship

Level 5
Building confidence in reading

Egg Fried Rice · Craig Saves the Day · Seasick · Dolphin Rescue · Hungry Floppy · Husky Adventure · Trapped! · Looking After Gran

Level 6
Reading with confidence

Gran's New Blue Shoes · Ice City · Save Pudding Wood · Uncle Max · Hairy-Scary Monster · Mountain Rescue · The Lost Voice · Secret of the Sands

Read with Biff, Chip and Kipper Collections:

Up You Go and Other Stories · Kipper's Rhymes and Other Stories · Six in a Bed and Other Stories · Funny Fish and Other Stories · Picnic Time and Other Stories · The Fizz-Buzz and Other Stories · Floppy and the Bone

I Can Trick a Tiger and Other Stories · The Moon Jet and Other Stories · Dragon Danger and Other Stories · Husky Adventure · Looking After Gran and Other Stories · Hairy-Scary Monster and Other Stories · Secret of the Sands and Other Stories

Every collection includes phonics and stories using everyday language

Phonics support

Flashcards are a really fun way to practise phonics and build reading skills. **Age 3+**

My Phonics Kit is designed to support you and your child as you practise phonics together at home. It includes stickers, workbooks, interactive eBooks, support for parents and more! **Age 5+**

Read Write Inc. Phonics: A range of fun rhyming stories to support decoding skills. **Age 4+**

Songbirds Phonics: Lively and engaging phonics stories from former Children's Laureate, Julia Donaldson. **Age 4+**

Helping your child's learning with free eBooks, essential tips and fun activities
www.oxfordowl.co.uk